The Solar System Glossary

Rotate: ....
....
....
....

Saturn: ....
....
....
....

Star: ....
....
....
....

Tilt: ....
....
....
....

Universe: ....
....
....

Satellite: ....
....
....
....

Solar System: ....
....
....
....

Sun: ....
....
....
....

Uranus: ....
....
....
....

Venus: ....
....
....

1 — Solar System

- The word **solar** means .....

- Our solar system is made up of a sun, 8 ...., a ....
  ...., ..., asteroids and ....

2 — Where Are We?

- Our solar system is in a
  .... called ....
  ....

- There are at least **two hundred**
  .... **stars** in The Milky Way.

3 — The Universe

- There are approximately ....
  .... galaxies in
  the ....
  - that we can see so far!

4 How Big?

- As .... get better, we can see more and more ....

5 The Sun

- The .... **is the largest object in our** ....

- All the .... in our solar system .... the Sun.

I'm the biggest object in the solar system!

6 Light

- The **Sun is a** ....
that emits (gives out) ....

- We can see the .... and
.... in our solar system.

- This is because the ....
from the Sun is .... off
them.

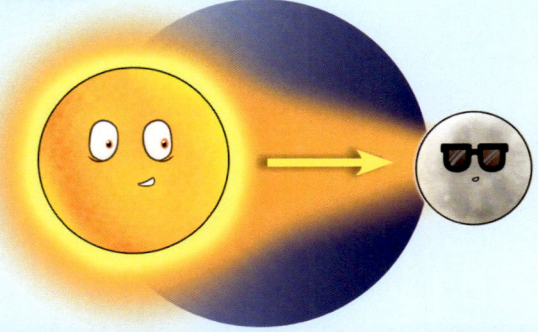

7 Heat
(not tested in CE)

- The Sun is about ....
degrees Celsius at its center.

- It is the .... of
most life on this planet.

I'm hot stuff AND so important!

2

8 How Long Is A Year?

- **One** .... is the time that it takes for a planet to complete **one** .... around the ....

- The .... the planet is away from the ...., the longer the year is!

9 Order of the Planets

- The Universe is huge.

- We use a unit called .... years.

- A light .... is the .... traveled by light in 1 year.

- The closest star to the Earth is .... light years away.

> Light moves at
> 300,000,000 M/S
> In 1 year light travels
> .... km = 1 light year

10 Complete the Rhyme to Learn The Planets!

This will help you learn the order of the planets away from the Sun!

Why not make up your own rhyme?

My	....
....	....
Easy	....
....	....
....	....
....	....
Up	....
....	....

Fill in the blanks using these words to help you...

year tilted day faster longer spin 23 250 closest
88 furthest 60,190 axis slower half

11 Quicker on Mercury!
(not tested in CE)

- A .... **on Mercury** (the .... planet to the Sun), lasts about .... **Earth days!**

- A **year on Neptune** (the .... planet from the Sun), lasts about .... **Earth days!**

12 Axis

- Planets spin on their ....

- The axis may be upright or .... The tilt on the **Earth's** ...., is .... **degrees.**

13 How Long Is A Day?

- One .... is the time that it takes for a planet to complete one .... on its ....

- The .... the planet **spins,** the longer the .... lasts!

14 Question Time!
(not tested in CE)

- A school day on **Venus** would last about .... times .... than ours!

- Does this mean Venus spins faster or slower than the Earth?

....

- A school day on Saturn, would last about .... as long as ours!

- Does Saturn spin faster or slower than the Earth? ....

4

Fill in the blanks using these words to help you...
hottest   Earth   night   heat   darkness   Sun   position
shadows   day   angle   vertical

15 Day and Night

daytime

Light rays

night time

As the Earth spins, **one side** of it **faces the ....**

That side is ..... **time.**

The other side is in ....

That side is .... **time!**

16 Temperature On Our Planet

It is .... where the **Sun's rays hit** the .... **vertically.**

As the .... spins, the .... of the sun appears to change. .... change length as this happens.

at an.............

....

at an ....

The Length of an Earth Day

Because **the Earth** is .... **on its axis**, as we orbit the Sun, the .... **of day changes.**

The **Earth** takes ..... **hours** to spin on its ..... This is **one Earth** ....!

The Earth's rotation around the Sun
Summer
Winter
The Earth's rotation around the Sun

In Winter, there are .... days and .... nights.

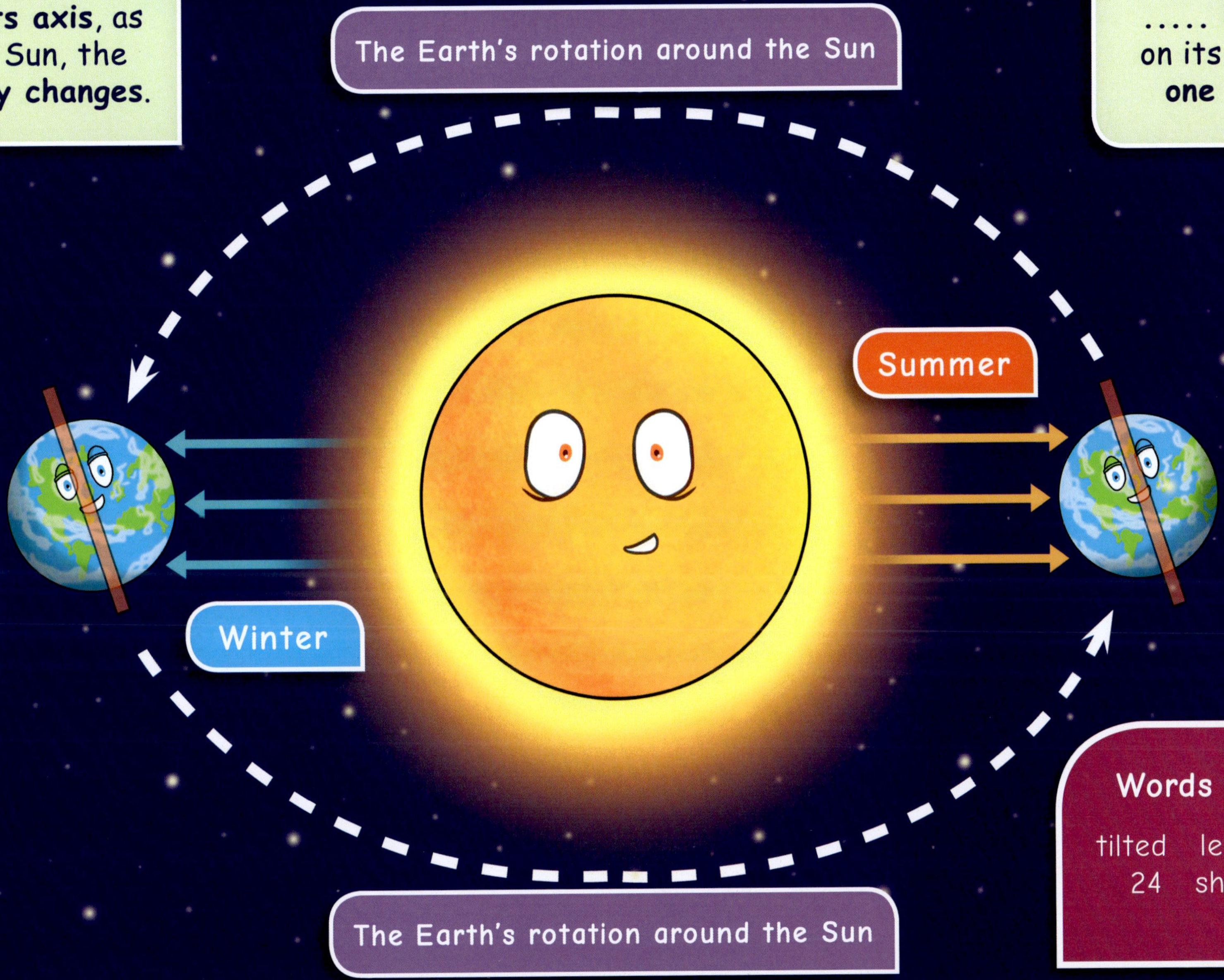

In Summer, there are .... days and .... nights.

Words to help you...

tilted length day axis
24 shorter longer

Fill in the blanks using these words to help you...
Australia North Sun closest hot Poles terrestrial Earth
elliptical rocky seasons circular temperature equator
gas giants oval circle directly

17 **Orbiting**
(not tested in CE)

- The four .... planets to the sun are called space planets.

- This means they are **like** ....

- These four .... planets have nearly perfect .... **orbits**.

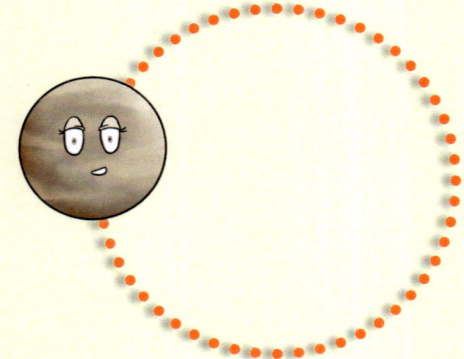

18 **Orbiting**
(not tested in CE)

- The larger outer four planets (known as ....) have .... **orbits**.

- Elliptical orbits are where the planet orbits in an .... **shape**, not in a perfect ....

19 **The Seasons**

- The .... we have and the .... depends on where you live on this planet.

- The .... and **South** .... **never** point directly at the .... This means they will never be ....

- The hottest countries lie near or on the ...., like South Africa and ....

- They spend much of their time pointing .... at the Sun.

Spring

Winter

Summer

Autumn

20   **The Moon Orbiting Earth**

The **Moon** is a **natural** .... that .... our planet.

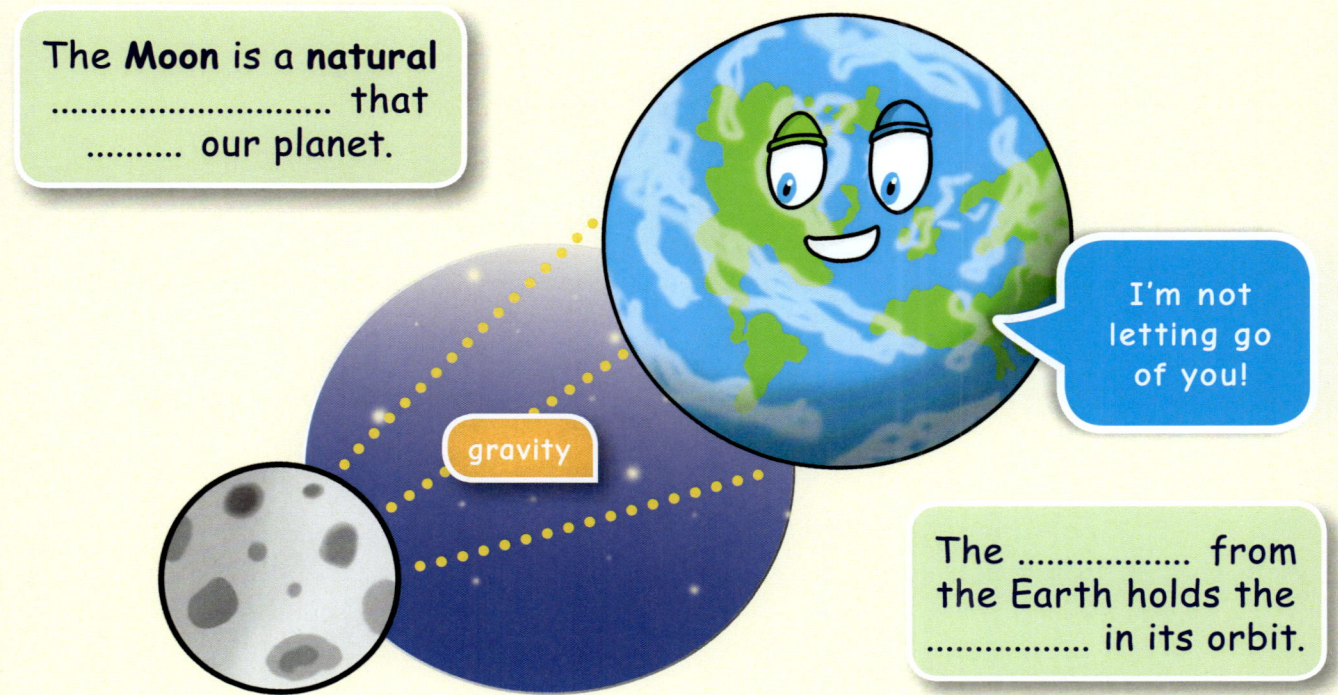

gravity

I'm not letting go of you!

The .... from the Earth holds the .... in its orbit.

21   **Draw the planets in our solar system.**
(Use the rhyme to put them in the right places!)

The .... from the .... holds all the .... in their **orbits**.

22 The Tides
(not tested in CE)

- .... from the **Moon** pulls on the .... of our planet.

- It makes the oceans .... up.

- As the Earth .... on its axis, the oceans are **bulged** in .... areas.

- This makes the .... **rise and fall** every 12 hours.

....

.... Tide

Earth spinning

.... Tide

....

The oceans .... out into a high tide due to the **spinning** of the ....

23 The Lunar Phase

- It takes the **Moon** about .... **days** to **orbit** us.

- **The** .... is how much of the Moon can be seen from ....

24 The Lunar Phase
(not tested in CE)

- The Lunar Phase depends on the position of the ...., ... and ....

REMEMBER!

We can only see the Moon because light from the Sun is .... from it!

Phases of the Moon
(not tested in CE)

Colour sections of each Moon black to show the different phases of the Moon. Number 2 has been done for you.

1

2

8

3

7

4

6

5

When the Moon is on the opposite side to the Sun, the whole Moon .... sunlight.

This is called a ..... Moon.

Stages of the Moon's orbit

1	2	3	4	5	6	7	8
new moon	waxing crescent	first quarter	waxing gibbous	full moon	waning gibbous	last quarter	waning crescent

25   **A Lunar Eclipse - draw a diagram to show the positions of the Sun, Moon and Earth**

- A **lunar eclipse** is when the
  .... is in the ....
  of the ....

- It only happens during
  a ...., when the
  ...., ..., and
  Moon are **in line**.

- There can be up to
  3 .... **eclipses**
  per year.

26   **A Solar Eclipse - draw a diagram to show the positions of the Sun, Moon and Earth**

- A **solar eclipse** happens when the ....
  passes .... the Sun and the Earth.

- The Sun is seen as a
  .... **disc**. It ....
  around the edges.

- It only happens during
  a .... when the
  Earth, Moon and Sun
  are .... **in line**.

- A .... solar eclipse
  happens somewhere on this
  planet, ... every three years!

Fill in the blanks using these words to help you...
life   109   6,000°C   solar system   460°C   size   70%
orbit   Mercury   closest   88   24°C   atmosphere

27   **The Sun**

- The Sun is .... **times bigger** than the Earth.

- It has an average surface **temperature** of ....

28   **Mercury**

- .... is less than half the size of the Earth.

- It is the .... planet to the Sun.

- It takes just .... **days** to .... the **Sun**.

29   **Venus**

- Venus is about the **same** .... as Earth.

- But it has a surface temperature of ....!

30   **Earth**

- Earth is .... **water**, with an .... that contains **oxygen**.

- It has an average surface temperature of ....

- It is the only **known planet** in our .... that can support ....

31   Mars

- Mars is about .... the size of Earth.

- It has .... **Moons** (also known as ....).

- It would take astronauts ....
  .... to reach Mars!

32   Jupiter

- Jupiter is about .... **times bigger** than Earth, and it has .... **Moons!**

- It is the first of the ....

- A day on Jupiter is just .... hours long but its year is nearly .... Earth years long!

33   Saturn

- Saturn is .... **times bigger** than Earth and it has .... **Moons** and 30 ......!

- The surface of Saturn is **liquid** ....

34   Uranus

- Uranus is titled ..... on its axis, more than any other main planet.

- It has a surface temperature of ....

35   Neptune

- .... on Neptune is nearly the **same** as on ....

- Neptune has .... Moons and 5 ....

36   Pluto

- Pluto is a .... about .... the size of Earth.

- It is .... **kilometres away** from the Sun.

37   Dwarf Planets

- **Dwarf** planets are planets **smaller** than ....

- The first five recognised dwarf planets are ...., **Pluto**, ..., ... **and** ....

38   Comets

- Most .... are just a few kilometres in ....

- **Comets** are made of **ice**, ..., and small pieces of **rock**.

14

39 Halley's Comets

- When comets pass close to the ......, the heat **vapourises** the ....

- This creates a **trail of** .... particles

- .... can be seen from Earth every 75 to 76 years!

40 Satellites

- .... are moons, planets, or .... that .... **a planet or star.**

- Earth is one of the .... satellites.

- The .... is the Earth's satellite.

41 Asteroids

- Asteroids are **small, rocky** .... that orbit the ....

- If all the .... were joined together, they would still not be as big as our ....

42 Asteroid Belt

- The .... is a doughtnut-shaped ring between the orbits of .... and ....